AN IRISH COUNTRY DIARY

THIS DIARY BELONGS TO

_____

AN IRISH COUNTRY DIARY
ALICE TAYLOR

including

COUNTRY LIFE
THROUGH THE SEASONS

with paintings by

MILDRED ANNE BUTLER

by Jim Canning

BRANDON

First published 1988
Brandon Ireland & UK Ltd
Dingle, Co. Kerry, Ireland.

Diary text © Alice Taylor 1988
Country Life Through the Seasons © Jim Canning 1988
Compilation © Brandon Ireland & UK Ltd 1988
Mildred Anne Butler paintings reproduced by permission of Jim Canning
Country Life Through the Seasons is an expanded version of an article first published
in *Ireland of the Welcomes*, July-August 1988

ISBN 0 86322 102 5

Design & makeup: Design II and Steve MacDonogh
Typesetting: Typeworkshop
Printed and bound by Richard Clay Ltd.

◡ Thinking Time

WELCOME TO MY diary. In a diary is a record of a private life where one year of living is encompassed between the covers. It may be very factual but still it is a picture in words of you and you alone.

My father kept a diary all his life. It contains no flights of fancy, just farm records, and still in its own way it is his story. An entry for 18 March 1925 reads: "Carried five heifers to the fair and sold them for £36-5s and a cow for £13-10s." That entry paints a picture for me of my father in the early dawn, driving his cattle up from the fields by the river and setting out to walk the three miles to the fair. Another entry reads: "Bought a pair of boots for 10/- that would be 50p in today's money. Changed times indeed!

A casual remark is thrown in after some of the entries and it introduces me to the young man that was my father, many years before I was born. Spoken words are carried away on the breeze of time but the written word is recorded for posterity and acts as a link between different generations.

One day, standing in a printing office, I saw a notice and was so impressed that I copied it down. I got a few strange looks as I knelt on the floor transcribing the following:

This is
A Printing Office
crossroads of civilization
refuge of all the arts
against the ravages of time
armoury of fearless truth
against whispering rumour
incessant trumpet of trade.
From this place words may fly abroad
not to perish on waves of sound
not to vary with the writers hand
but fixed in time having been verified in proof

Friend you stand on sacred ground
This is A Printing Office.

As a child and teenager I kept a diary and in it was my own little world. At the top of our house was an attic which we called the "black loft" because it was dimly lit by one small dormer window. Here was the accumulation of years. The relegated life of the family downstairs found its way up here in many forms. Even the lives of previous generations were remembered here in old school books and high buttoned boots. The horses also were represented by old horse collars and saddles with trailing padding which hung from rafters shrouded with soft grey cobwebs.

Here, too, was the iron cot with its brass railings which had provided a teething ring for years of dribbling toddlers. This cot was designed to withstand robust youngsters but now the brass knobs were dented and battered and there under the sloping roof it rested, a relic of former days. Beside it stood the family cradle, made of strong cane and supported by two large timber rockers. It was sufficiently long to take a prone four-year-old who felt like a mid-day siesta but still did not want to leave the warm kitchen to go to the draughty upstairs rooms. It had stood in a nook under the stairs in the kitchen for many years until even the youngest felt it beneath his dignity to get into it. Now this, too, joined the other old childhood friends in the attic.

My mother collected old newspapers and there in the corner bundles of them formed pillars shrouded in dust. Parts of beehives rested here between the seasons as did rose-patterned chamber pots with matching jug and bowl, reserved for special visitors.

Part of the floorboards had sagged with the years to reveal the rafters of the parlour beneath.

You had to watch your step in case an unwary move might bring you through the ceiling of the parlour on top of an unsuspecting visitor.

Mice ran along the bare rafters and nested in the old horse collars. When the swallows came they nested around the dormer window and when the day was sunny and the window open, they flew in where they were joined by cheeky robins.

This was my "hidey hole." Here beneath the window I cleared a space and surrounded it by old trunks left by former generations of returning Yanks. Into this space I dragged a rickety table with one short leg, which I propped up with a red brick eased from our own kiln. This was my desk and here I recorded the daily happenings, real and imaginary, careful not to lean too heavily in any direction in case my woodworm-digested table would disintegrate beneath me. On this table could be created strange designs as a rambling pencil would uncover underground tunnels burrowed by energetic woodworm. Then clouds of white dust could be wafted gently along the table and brushed into gaping crevices at the other end.

Looking out the little window I could see down along the sloping green fields to the river valley, where the cattle grazed peacefully in the inches. Then the fields rose again, rolling into soft rounded hills and then disappearing into misty mountains. My little window was my viewfinder into the world of nature. Looking left I could see glimpses of the low stone bridge between the yellow furze. Straight ahead were the sprawling farmyards and to the right old Mike's cottage nesting in the trees.

As I wrote my diary here the world of nature coloured my writings. During the winter months I wrote till my fingers were as blue as the ink on the diary pages, while my legs froze in my long, black, knitted stockings. Up here in my draughty attic the luxury of heating was unheard of and also unquestioned. The winter scene penetrated my little attic hideaway. As the icicles hung from the slates above the window, it did not stretch the imagination too far to describe freezing winter scenes or be stirred to write:

Dear Lord
Does a cold anger
Fill your heart
Is it coming
Down in snow
As a blizzard
On the land
Are you weeping
Tears of ice
Have you frozen
All your love
Are the icicles
Of Heaven
A judgement
From above?

Sometimes the snow came serene and beautiful, covering my world under a soft white blanket. Then came the thaw and my bones softened out with the countryside and Spring breathed over the land. From this attic window I could watch the dawn creep over the countryside and cast fingers of light into the dim attic. The quieteness of the early dawn eases the mind gently into the new day which stretches out before us, waiting to be experienced. Each day is a new beginning and each year is a book with 365 blank pages to be filled in by us, as we go through it.

Let us open our book of the year and let the light pour gently on its early pages. All of us have our own book but each will write a different story and use this diary for different things.

Come with me through the pages of the year ahead and journey into the paintings of Mildred Anne Butler, enjoying the peace and serenity of the countryside. Make this diary your private world because in this hectic rush that is today we each need our own space and thinking time.

♪ Personal Notes

♫ Four Year Calendar
1988

	January
S	3 10 17 24 31
M	4 11 18 25
T	5 12 19 26
W	6 13 20 27
T	7 14 21 28
F	1 8 15 22 29
S	2 9 16 23 30

	February
S	7 14 21 28
M	1 8 15 22 29
T	2 9 16 23
W	3 10 17 24
T	4 11 18 25
F	5 12 19 26
S	6 13 20 27

	March
S	6 13 20 27
M	7 14 21 28
T	1 8 15 22 29
W	2 9 16 23 30
T	3 10 17 24 31
F	4 11 18 25
S	5 12 19 26

	April
S	3 10 17 24
M	4 11 18 25
T	5 12 19 26
W	6 13 20 27
T	7 14 21 28
F	1 8 15 22 29
S	2 9 16 23 30

	May
S	1 8 15 22 29
M	2 9 16 23 30
T	3 10 17 24 31
W	4 11 18 25
T	5 12 19 26
F	6 13 20 27
S	7 14 21 28

	June
S	5 12 19 26
M	6 13 20 27
T	7 14 21 28
W	1 8 15 22 29
T	2 9 16 23 30
F	3 10 17 24
S	4 11 18 25

	July
S	3 10 17 24 31
M	4 11 18 25
T	5 12 19 26
W	6 13 20 27
T	7 14 21 28
F	1 8 15 22 29
S	2 9 16 23 30

	August
S	7 14 21 28
M	1 8 15 22 29
T	2 9 16 23 30
W	3 10 17 24 31
T	4 11 18 25
F	5 12 19 26
S	6 13 20 27

	September
S	4 11 18 25
M	5 12 19 26
T	6 13 20 27
W	7 14 21 28
T	1 8 15 22 29
F	2 9 16 23 30
S	3 10 17 24

	October
S	2 9 16 23 30
M	3 10 17 24 31
T	4 11 18 25
W	5 12 19 26
T	6 13 20 27
F	7 14 21 28
S	1 8 15 22 29

	November
S	6 13 20 27
M	7 14 21 28
T	1 8 15 22 29
W	2 9 16 23 30
T	3 10 17 24
F	4 11 18 25
S	5 12 19 26

	December
S	4 11 18 25
M	5 12 19 26
T	6 13 20 27
W	7 14 21 28
T	1 8 15 22 29
F	2 9 16 23 30
S	3 10 17 24 31

ᓚ Four Year Calendar
1989

	January	February	March
S	1 8 15 22 29	5 12 19 26	5 12 19 26
M	2 9 16 23 30	6 13 20 27	6 13 20 27
T	3 10 17 24 31	7 14 21 28	7 14 21 28
W	4 11 18 25	1 8 15 22	1 8 15 22 29
T	5 12 19 26	2 9 16 23	2 9 16 23 30
F	6 13 20 27	3 10 17 24	3 10 17 24 31
S	7 14 21 28	4 11 18 25	4 11 18 25

	April	May	June
S	2 9 16 23 30	7 14 21 28	4 11 18 25
M	3 10 17 24	1 8 15 22 29	5 12 19 26
T	4 11 18 25	2 9 16 23 30	6 13 20 27
W	5 12 19 26	3 10 17 24 31	7 14 21 28
T	6 13 20 27	4 11 18 25	1 8 15 22 29
F	7 14 21 28	5 12 19 26	2 9 16 23 30
S	1 8 15 22 29	6 13 20 27	3 10 17 24

	July	August	September
S	2 9 16 23 30	6 13 20 27	3 10 17 24
M	3 10 17 24 31	7 14 21 28	4 11 18 25
T	4 11 18 25	1 8 15 22 29	5 12 19 26
W	5 12 19 26	2 9 16 23 30	6 13 20 27
T	6 13 20 27	3 10 17 24 31	7 14 21 28
F	7 14 21 28	4 11 18 25	1 8 15 22 29
S	1 8 15 22 29	5 12 19 26	2 9 16 23 30

	October	November	December
S	1 8 15 22 29	5 12 19 26	3 10 17 24 31
M	2 9 16 23 30	6 13 20 27	4 11 18 25
T	3 10 17 24 31	7 14 21 28	5 12 19 26
W	4 11 18 25	1 8 15 22 29	6 13 20 27
T	5 12 19 26	2 9 16 23 30	7 14 21 28
F	6 13 20 27	3 10 17 24	1 8 15 22 29
S	7 14 21 28	4 11 18 25	2 9 16 23 30

ᔰ Four Year Calendar
1990

	January				
S		7	14	21	28
M	1	8	15	22	29
T	2	9	16	23	30
W	3	10	17	24	31
T	4	11	18	25	
F	5	12	19	26	
S	6	13	20	27	

	February			
	4	11	18	25
	5	12	19	26
	6	13	20	27
	7	14	21	28
1	8	15	22	
2	9	16	23	
3	10	17	24	

	March			
	4	11	18	25
	5	12	19	26
	6	13	20	27
	7	14	21	28
1	8	15	22	29
2	9	16	23	30
3	10	17	24	31

	April				
S	1	8	15	22	29
M	2	9	16	23	30
T	3	10	17	24	
W	4	11	18	25	
T	5	12	19	26	
F	6	13	20	27	
S	7	14	21	28	

	May				
	6	13	20	27	
	7	14	21	28	
1	8	15	22	29	
2	9	16	23	30	
3	10	17	24	31	
4	11	18	25		
5	12	19	26		

	June			
	3	10	17	24
	4	11	18	25
	5	12	19	26
	6	13	20	27
	7	14	21	28
1	8	15	22	29
2	9	16	23	30

	July				
S	1	8	15	22	29
M	2	9	16	23	30
T	3	10	17	24	31
W	4	11	18	25	
T	5	12	19	26	
F	6	13	20	27	
S	7	14	21	28	

	August			
	5	12	19	26
	6	13	20	27
	7	14	21	28
1	8	15	22	29
2	9	16	23	30
3	10	17	24	31
4	11	18	25	

	September			
	2	9	16	23 30
	3	10	17	24
	4	11	18	25
	5	12	19	26
	6	13	20	27
	7	14	21	28
1	8	15	22	29

	October				
S		7	14	21	28
M	1	8	15	22	29
T	2	9	16	23	30
W	3	10	17	24	31
T	4	11	18	25	
F	5	12	19	26	
S	6	13	20	27	

	November			
	4	11	18	25
	5	12	19	26
	6	13	20	27
	7	14	21	28
1	8	15	22	29
2	9	16	23	30
3	10	17	24	

	December			
	2	9	16	23 30
	3	10	17	24 31
	4	11	18	25
	5	12	19	26
	6	13	20	27
	7	14	21	28
1	8	15	22	29

৶ Four Year Calendar
1991

January
S		6	13 20 27
M		7	14 21 28
T	1	8	15 22 29
W	2	9	16 23 30
T	3	10	17 24 31
F	4	11	18 25
S	5	12	19 26

February
S		3	10 17 24
M		4	11 18 25
T		5	12 19 26
W		6	13 20 27
T		7	14 21 28
F	1	8	15 22
S	2	9	16 23

March
S		3	10 17 24 31
M		4	11 18 25
T		5	12 19 26
W		6	13 20 27
T		7	14 21 28
F	1	8	15 22 29
S	2	9	16 23 30

April
S		7	14 21 28
M	1	8	15 22 29
T	2	9	16 23 30
W	3	10	17 24
T	4	11	18 25
F	5	12	19 26
S	6	13	20 27

May
S		5	12 19 26
M		6	13 21 27
T		7	14 20 28
W	1	8	15 22 29
T	2	9	16 23 30
F	3	10	17 24 31
S	4	11	18 25

June
S		2	9	16 23 30
M		3	10	17 24
T		4	11	18 25
W		5	12	19 26
T		6	13	20 27
F		7	14	21 28
S	1	8	15	22 29

July
S		7	14 21 28
M	1	8	15 22 29
T	2	9	16 23 30
W	3	10	17 24 31
T	4	11	18 25
F	5	12	19 26
S	6	13	20 27

August
S		4	11 18 25
M		5	12 19 26
T		6	13 20 27
W		7	14 21 28
T	1	8	15 22 29
F	2	9	16 23 30
S	3	10	17 24 31

September
S	1	8	15 22 29
M	2	9	16 23 30
T	3	10	17 24
W	4	11	18 25
T	5	12	19 26
F	6	13	20 27
S	7	14	21 28

October
S		6	13 20 27
M		7	14 21 28
T	1	8	15 22 29
W	2	9	16 23 30
T	3	10	17 24 31
F	4	11	18 25
S	5	12	19 26

November
S		3	10 17 24
M		4	11 18 25
T		5	12 19 26
W		6	13 20 27
T		7	14 21 28
F	1	8	15 22 29
S	2	9	16 23 30

December
S	1	8	15 22 29
M	2	9	16 23 30
T	3	10	17 24 31
W	4	11	18 25
T	5	12	19 26
F	6	13	20 27
S	7	14	21 28

♫ January

THE COUNTRYSIDE IN January is going through a hibernation period. It is withdrawn from us, all its power and beauty buried within. It is hatching its resources for the year ahead and away deep down in the earth life is recreating itself.

Life on the farm is in harmony with nature because the tempo of work slows down almost to a standstill. There is no activity out in the fields where nature shrouds the land in a veil of frost, or a blanket of snow or sheets of rain render the soil too soft for the animals. They are all gathered into the farmyard where they are sheltered from the winter cold. The animals themselves have ceased their productivity as the hens do not lay their eggs in the frosty weather and most of the cows now in calf no longer produce milk. Even the cows carrying hidden life within, move ponderously, for they too sense the slowing down of the rhythm.

The country at this time of year has its own beauty, a stark, harsh beauty whereby the trees are bare skeletons silhouetted against the skyline and the rivers are pools of black secrets. Nature is teaching us a lesson, that we too need to draw things within outselves and enrich our own reserves. January, the hatching month of the year, is the time to satisfy our deep creative needs. We fill our lives with practical activities but each of us has a creative side which if left unfulfilled, will decay in frustration and discontent. There is a deep glow of satisfaction to be experienced when we create something with our hands and minds. A woman knitting a jumper is a picture of contentment; a man running his hand over a piece of timber he has just planed, feeling its texture, often has an expression of intense pleasure on his face. Both are experiencing the joy of creation.

This is the month that opens the door of the

year. Opening the door to any new experience should be filled with a sense of challenge and expectation but many of us are at a very low ebb at this time of year.

We do not like you January
You are cold, hard and wet
Gripping the countryside
In a frozen death
Christmas cheer is darkened
Virgin snow to slush
Howling icy winds
Replace the holy hush
Dark and reptile roads
With black ice out of sight
Trap the cheery driver
And kill him in the night
January you're the Judas
Of the twelve around the year
You make the lonely lonelier
And the old to fear.

For many of us January is our grey month, giving us the feeling that nature has abandoned us. Perhaps we could learn from nature and make January our hatching month when we cultivate our own inner resources in a way that is right for us.

This January, let us imitate nature and burrow deep within our being and discover things about ourselves to fortify us for the year ahead. In this way January will be our storehouse and we can open the door and enter the year with courage in our step.

January

♪ January

♪ January

January

♪ January

♪ January

February

THIS IS THE month when the countryside sends out little spurts of life, as if to tell us that all is well and that she is about to come out of hibernation. But just as the winding down of the earth's life in the autumn was a gradual, unhurried process now, too, the opening up is a slow, tentative awakening. Like a baby fluttering open its eyelids, the first soft flush of spring appears. Our frozen winter souls begin to thaw in answer to her gentle warmth.

You soft winter day
Shining through the cold
You are a welcome stranger
Bringing warmth to my bones.

And yet spring is like a pretty, flirtatious Victorian lady, sometimes casting on us a glance warm with promise only again to disappear behind her winter fan, leaving us to cool in the winter winds of her icy disdain. And just when we begin to feel that she is gone for good and the cold of winter settles over our hearts again, back she steals and takes us by surprise in an unexpected corner.

Daffodil how good you are
To peep above the earth
In these barren windy days
Yours is a joyous birth.

And so throughout the month of February spring plays a game of hide-and-seek with us but the promise is there with the little buds appearing above the brown earth and now the door of the new year is opening wider with each day.

In the farmyard new life is appearing and the first to make their presence felt are the baby calves. Cows are patient, gentle creatures who bear the pangs of calving with soulful moans. Once their calves are safely delivered, they lick them dry and then get back to the business of milk production. One of the memories of my childhood was going into the cow house, where late at night the cows lay bedded in yellow straw, all contentedly chewing the cud. They exuded an air of total relaxation and peace, filling the stalls with their warm and earthy fragrance.

Now, too, it could happen that spring, having lulled us into a sense of false security by staying for a few days, could suddenly disappear and the snow would come billowing over the fields, covering us in soft white drifts. My earliest memory of snow is of 1947 when the entire country was buried beneath six-foot-deep drifts for many weeks. We walked over ditches and gates which were buried in hard-packed snow. That year I got my first pair of wellingtons. In the innocence of childhood I thought that you could not get wet in wellingtons even if you walked into snow waist high. My illusions about the magic boots were soon shattered.

But the birds are the real heralds of the spring. During the winter, all their energies have been channelled into survival but now they sense that deliverance is near; they welcome the softer days and send their messages of hope and gladness to brighten our days.

And you my feathered friend
Sing on that winter tree
You bring comfort to my heart
And keep hope alive in me.

♪ February

February

February

February

February

February

～ March

OH BROWN PLOUGHED field
What an ancient skill
Is in your turned sod
A skill inherited
By generations of earthy men
Beneath the sheltering trees
You cover the hillside
In a cloak of brown velvet
What a softness is yours
You are an open book
Yet to be written
The virginity of the upturned sod
Waiting to be fertilised
By the hands of man
And nurtured by the warmth of nature.

This is the month when man shows his trust in nature and God by sowing in the earth the seeds of the future and having done this leaves it to those powers greater than himself to do the rest. March, like most creative characters, is temperamental, blowing hot and cold or, as the old people used to say, coming in like a lamb and going out like a lion or vice versa. The winds of March wake us up after the sleep of winter and blow the cobwebs out of our brains. This is the season that finally brings to life the entire countryside and the turning of the sod by the plough is the final routing of the winter inertia.

Now the gardeners begin to move and the pruner is brought into action and dead rosewood is cut away in preparation for the new growth.

A walk at this time of year is an invigorating experience with the sharp wind blowing through your hair and whipping up your blood circulation. Last March, caught out in a sudden drenching shower, I sheltered under a roadside tree swaying on the ditch. Sitting on the mossy ditch I felt the roots of the tree moving beneath me as the howling wind blew its upper-most branches about in angry confusion. The wind and the tree were engaged in a duel of strength and I was a silent witness. Beside the tree was a derelict old house with a rusty, sagging, galvanised roof and the wind played a mournful lament through its gaping windows and down its old stone chimney, which the cows now called their own. Welcoming smoke would never again rise skywards from this abandoned little house and I wondered what was its story. Should "Gone to America" be written on its tombstone?

Vacuum womb house
Contracted into another life
An afterbirth remaining
Whisper and shadows
Of another day
Memory in its
Soft grey clouds
Wafting through the rooms
Webbing here
The part of me
That belongs
The living that was blended
Through these stones
So I take with me
Past soul of this house
And leave behind
Part of mine.

Whenever I see a derelict house it triggers off my imagination to see in the mind's eye the life that once was there. Each of these old houses is a book and the story of its life is written on the pages of the hearts of the children reared there and who now live in far away places.

♪ March

♪ March

March

March

March

March

April

APRIL IS THE month that kicks completely open the door of the new year and the last shadows of winter are finally evicted. The year is now up and runing on "Ar muin na muice" as the old people would say when things were going well. Now the swallows glide in from foreign places, bringing with them the first smell of summer. Oh, the thrill when I was young to be the first to sight the swallows! They came back to the stables, the stalls and the barns where their cobweb-draped nests waited to be spring cleaned and they got straight down to work, gliding in and out, totally preoccupied with the business. Soon the nests with their earth-encrusted exteriors took on a lived-in appearance, with fresh twigs and feathers decorating their door steps. We could never get to see the eggs as they arrived because the swallows believed in high living and the nests clung solidly to obscure corners under arching rafters.

Now all the birds welcome the brighter days with the full-throated volume of the dawn chorus. As the first fingers of light penetrate the night sky, a faint twittering is heard, to be joined gradually by other voices until all break forth in homage to the new day. There is no lovelier way to start your day than to rise before the world gets up and welcome in the dawn with the birds.

Let me steal five minutes
To welcome in the dawn
To caress its dewy fingers
As they creep across the lawn
To watch beneath a misty tree
The sun roll back the night
Its beams transfusing darkness
With pink translucent light
To hear the birds awake
With delight to greet the day
Let their happiness infuse me

To meet my day their way
Let this tranquil scene give balance
To the busy day ahead
To create a tranquil pool
For withdrawal inside my head.

April also brings the young lambs frisking in the soft green fields where the early buttercups and primroses are quietly peeping up to see if all is well with the world. Nature is gradually shedding its old grey coat and donning a soft green mantle. Our world is changing from a harsh, scraggy old man into a soft, shy young girl in the first flush of youth. The sap is rising and it is the time when we are told a young man's fancy turns to love and even the not so young may feel the urge, though it may not extend any further than their heads. We should celebrate the spring and let the fresh young world of nature, now at its peak, pour into our hearts and minds. Whether in the countryside or in your own garden, go out in the early morning, close your eyes and smell the earth and absorb it in your bones because we all come from the earth and our journey carries us back there again, so let's keep close to it and stay in harmony with God's world. Open your eyes and let the fresh, moist green of spring give you a new vision of life. This is a beautiful world, let's enjoy it.

April

April

April

April

April

♪ April

May

A N OLD IRISH belief was that on May Day
you washed your face in the early morning
dew and the fairies gave you a beautiful
complexion. What a lovely thought! It conjures up
images of fairy magic and warm dew. May, to me,
will always be the barefoot month. It was then we
abandoned our shoes and stockings to run
barefoot through the dew-drenched grass. The feel
of the warm dew running down your legs and
tickling between your toes is an experience that
nobody should be denied. So, if you never ran
barefoot through the sun-warmed, dewy grass of
the early morning, let this May bring you that
lovely sensation. Some day when you decide to
abandon routine, dance through a dew-drenched
field and fling your arms wide to embrace the
beauties of nature and run free for one morning
from the trappings of responsibility. It will
rejuvenate your spirits and give you a happy
perspective on life. The cows and the sheep will
take no notice. They have done it all their lives. Is
there anything as lovely as the young lambs
prancing around with the joy of living? What the
farmer would think of your activities I cannot
guarantee. But then maybe you might come upon
one who would be glad to celebrate May Day with
you!

May is also the bluebell month, and how they
carpet the woods with their beauty! Here where I
live in Innishannon, Dromkeen Wood in May is a
sight to behold. Planted on the side of a sloping
hill, with a path meandering between the trees,
the bluebells stretch as far as the eye can see to
disappear in a blue haze over the hill. Though
bluebells do not lend themselves to flower
arranging and their vase life is very short, still I
love to see them in the kitchen tumbling out over
the side of the old jug into which they are usually

thrust. They need no arranging, and they bring the freshness of nature into the kitchen.

Give me a bunch
Of dew-fresh flowers
What if they do not last
I cannot live in the future
The present is all I ask.

In May, too, the children, like the flowers, come out in their summer dresses to brighten up our days. Children have the freedom of May in their hearts and like the white butterflies they flutter through our lives spreading sunshine.

How wondrous a baby
A beautiful creation
Fresh from the hand of God
Surely angels stand sentinel
Over this heavenly being
And when in her sleep she smiles
A pure happy smile
She is playing
With the angels
In her dreams.

In May the world is young and children are in total harmony with it because they are young too. So give them time to enjoy the countryside and follow the white butterflies that belong to the young alone.

May

May

May

May

May

ᔓ May

♪ June

HAVE YOU EVER sat on a river bank early on a June morning, feeling the sun warm on your back and watching a swan sail majestically by? A river surrounded by woods is twice blessed with beauty on its bank and again mirrored in its depths. The swan with her soft white plumage and the wisping white clouds reflected in the river are the only shades of brightness in this green sheltered haven. I sit here and let the quietness of the water wash over me and ebb into the remote corners of my mind. Suddenly, the swan sighting something more interesting up the river, takes to the air with a might splash and a loud flapping of wings and disappears from view, leaving the water rippling for a few minutes. Now there is only myself, the river and the wood, or so I think until a water hen silently, like a black ballerina, skims the water just below me. I sit motionless lest even the slightest movement would send her seeking cover. This is her world, not mine, so I must not intrude. After a few minutes she disappears under the over-hanging moist ferns. The dripping ferns bring to mind that the stone on which I had sat myself down has disappeared into the soft damp earth, which is now soaking up through my lower regions. My old friend, Bill, used to say "You'll get bumtism." I doubt if that is even a word in the English dictionary but, like most words coined to describe a situation, it is self-explanatory.

I ease myself quietly from my viewing point on the river bank and climb up the slippery slope, using the tree trunks as anchors and pulleys. Having been reared in the country and gone to school through the fields, you never forget how to climb steep hills, manipulate yourself over briar-covered ditches and get across rickety iron gates. It becomes second nature to you.

Back on the firm pathway, the earth is soft beneath my feet as the river glints occasionally through the dense greenery. Sometimes the sun breaks through the greening branches of the over-hanging trees, filling the wood with dappled sunlight. The sunlight and the riverlight turn the woods into a world of light and shadows and an infinite variety of greens. Thank God for woods to walk through and rivers to sit beside. We are surely living in a beautiful world.

June

June

June

June

June

♪ June

COUNTRY LIFE
THROUGH THE SEASONS
the paintings of
MILDRED ANNE BUTLER
by Jim Canning

MILDRED ANNE BUTLER viewed and painted rural life through the seasons, and she captured all the activities of domestic and farm life. Despite her travels on the Continent, the main thrust of her work came from the life she knew and loved around Kilmurry and the villages of County Kilkenny.

Mildred Anne Butler was born in 1858 in Kilmurry, near Thomastown in County Kilkenny. It was to remain her home for life and furthermore the family estate was to provide her with material for the very best of her watercolours. She was the

Trees in January

Landscape with Meadow in Foreground

great-niece of Simon Butler, first President of The United Irishman, prominent in the movement for Catholic Emancipation and parlimentary reform. An unusual position for a Protestant country gentleman in Ireland at the time.

Like her father, Captain Edward Butler, she began to keep sketch books from the time she was about twenty. He was an army officer who travelled extensively and was an excellent draftsman and amateur artist. He published in 1841 *South African Sketches: Illustrations of the wild life of a hunter on the frontier of Cape Colony*. His work had wit and charm, though much was somewhat creepy and bizarre - full of snakes and weird atmospheric effects. Some of his watercolours remain, but bear no resemblance whatsover to the work of Mildred Anne. He died in 1881 before his daughter had developed as an artist and had no influence on her style as a painter, though presumably he had encouraged her talents.

She was one of a family of six of which two of her brothers had army careers, but none of them married. Despite chronic rheumatism she outlived them all and inherited Kilmurry.

In becoming an artist Mildred Anne was following a path taken by numerous Irish gentlewomen of her generation, as painting, particularly in watercolour, was considered one of the very few respectable occupations which educated upper class women could take up in late nineteenth century Ireland. Furthermore, it was socially acceptable to travel and exhibit their work. Indeed, a great number of Irish women had been drawing since the early part of the eighteenth century.

Mildred Anne Butler's early work showed little promise but the breakthrough seemed to have come when she went to London and studied under

Paul Jacob Naftel who, it would appear, was known to her family previously, as he had painted in Ireland in 1861. He proved to be a great influence as did her next tutor, the animal painter Frank Calderon who, despite the fact that he was many years younger than her, had been exhibiting regularly at the Royal Academy from 1881. It was undoubtedly he who steered her in the direction of making countless watercolours and drawings of cattle and of birds which were to be the basis for some of her most delightful work. One of these - *And Straight Against the Great Array* - was shown at the Royal Academy in 1893 and is now in the National Gallery of Ireland.

One can hardly image a more idyllic scene that that of an elegant Edwardian Lady seated at her easel among the wild flowers in the heart of Ireland's richest landscape, painting what she saw. To the passing observer she would have seemed like the central figure in a perfect setting. Her stage was provided by nature. In the distance was Kilmurry, the elegant eighteenth century house where she was born. Around her were the fields, woodlands, ponds and the river which made up the three hundred and fifty acre family estate in the townland of Thomastown in County Kilkenny.

If this was the stage then the actors must have been the cattle grazing or resting beneath the trees; sheep in the distant hills; wood pigeons in the trees and young coots and chicks darting across the pond by the oak woodland walk behind her house. During her life as a painter, Mildred Anne Butler was to record it all, perfectly, in numerous delicate and evocative watercolours and drawings, the great majority of which were discovered in her old studio at the family home, some forty years after her death.

In winter she painted the leafless trees as well

Phlox, Roses and other Flowers in a Herbaceous Border

Wisteria

as the ducks on the pond by the house. Many of her interiors of Kilmurry, according to her diary notes, were painted in winter. An old lady reading by the soft light of a paraffin lamp sitting by a cosy log fire, a cape draped across a chair, or a simple doorway at Kilmurry were all given her attention.

In spring she painted the wild fowl on the river as well as the sheep with their lambs in the fields. She painted the cows and calves grazing and frolicking in the fields and in their sheds in the farmyard as they fed on hay and turnips.

Summer was haymaking time. She painted delightful watercolours of the haymakers at Kilmurry with horses and hay carts, recording meticulously this important annual task; mowing with horse-drawn machines, stooking in the fields and finally, taking it to the farmyard where it was forked into great reeks.

Summer also brought wisteria and a mass of colour on the walls and around the windows of Kilmurry. Her *Wisteria and Other Blossoms around an Open Window* is one of her best loved works. The turn of the century saw the gardens of Ireland at their very finest. Kilmurry was no exception and ranked high among the best of them, and there are many sketches, drawings and watercolours of her sister Isabel (Issy) in the garden. Immaculately laid out and nestling among the pastures of Kilkenny, its herbaceous borders, avenues of flowering trees and a conservatory full of potted plants presented a wealth of colour for Mildred Anne to paint. And paint it she did. These were the perfect settings for her studies of children playing, cats stalking birds and Isabel busy among the flowers and shrubs.

Summer, too, was holiday time, both at home and abroad. Mildred for many years took her holidays at Tramore in County Waterford, where she painted the morning mist over the sea, and obviously delighted in achieving spectacular effects of shafts of light entwining the sea vapours. She watched and sketched as the children happily played and made sandcastles on the Tramore beaches.

From what we see from her sketch books her first travels on the Continent were in the Summer fo 1885 when she went with a relation, Lady French. In subsequent years they travelled through France, to the Swiss lakes and into Italy. She was a great observer and she painted it all, from Kilmurry to Lake Como and back through Paris where she painted fountains, men in shadowy acade doorways and horses and carts in the street.

In her wanderings much nearer home she never tired of painting what was closest to her. Trees and foliage, wild flowers in the fields and on the river banks. In her *Among The Woods* she recorded the perfectly still late Autumn morning, its silence disturbed only by the flutter of pigeons' wings as they took flight in the early morning mist.

Autumn on the farm at Kilmurry was harvest time and she recorded it perfectly. The old steam-driven thresher at work was a favourite. One can almost smell the steam and sense the dust and chaff from the threshing mill as the farm workers, men and women, spent three days at the annual threshing. Oats and barley were stored in the great lofts for feeding the workhorses, cattle and other animals on the farm. Straw was piled in reeks beside the hay. Surplus grain was sold to the local millers at Thomastown and Bennettsbridge. Here it was crushed and rolled by the millstones powered by giant waterwheels on the Rivers Nore and Barrow. Some of these old mills remain and one or two still stone-grind wheat for bread

In a Village Street

An Autumn Day

making.

The hunt was also a great favourite: Mildred followed the huntsmen and pack around Kilkenny and there are many colourful scenes of hounds chasing the fox across the open Kilkenny countryside. She was not afraid, either, of depicting the more gruesome part of Irish country life: the kill, as the hounds closed in on their prey; a dead magpie suspended in a leafless tree; a cat with a dead bird or rabbit, or, indeed, a dead decaying crow in the farmyard.

Reviews of her exhibitions from the early 1890s singled her out for being most unconventional and for the "curious" subjects which she painted. According to art historian Hilary Pyle the Belfast *News Letter* on 11 November 1893 referred to her "very clever treatment of her difficult and unpicturesque subject in *The Kitchen Garden* and on 8 November 1895 mentioned her "proficiency with catchy subjects."

Hilary Pyle points out also that by 1903 she was regarded as being in the forefront of contemporary painters in watercolour and had not only been asked to contribute to a portfolio of sketches for the Duchess of York's wedding present but also to the Coronation gift for King Edward VII.

Despite the fact that Mildred Anne came from a family background where she did not need to earn her living she was obviously very capable of doing so from her paintings. Besides selling her watercolours in Ireland she was also selling regularly to English collectors through the Royal Watercolour Society Gallery in London and she received many commissions from the Gallery for her cattle, bird and rural scenes which were particularly popular in England at the time.

Her first major success, the purchase in 1896 by the Chantrey Bequest of the *Morning Bath* made her reputation. The picture was bought for the

Tate Gallery for £50. In the following year Lady
Cadogan, the Vicereine in Dublin, gave the
Princess of Wales one of Mildred Anne Butler's
watercolours. Earlier in 1893 she had been
included in a book of watercolours given by the
Lady Artists to Queen Mary, then Princess May,
on her marriage to the Duke of York. Later Queen
Mary bought a watercolour by her and in 1922
Mildred painted a tiny picture of crows for Queen
Mary's doll's house at Windsor. She was elected an
Associate of the Royal Watercolour Society in
1896, but only became a full member many years
later in 1937, by which date she had given up
painting because of her acute arthritis. She died in
1941 and for the next forty years her reputation
languished and she fell into obscurity.

In 1980 some four hundred watercolours,
drawings and sketches together with notes, letters
and diaries were discovered, as she had left them
in her studio in Kilmurry. Some were sold in
Ireland and some were sold at a studio sale at
Christies in London. Interest quickly rekindled
itself and galleries, collectors and dealers rushed
to buy. Fortunately a great number of her
paintings either stayed in Ireland or were brought
back to Ireland by purchasers.

The National Gallery of Ireland purchased
seven very fine watercolours for their permanent
collection and in their catalogue of acquisitions for
1981/82, the Director of the National Gallery,
Homan Potterton, described the find of the
watercolours, as "the phenomenon of the century."
The Gallery proudly showed these watercolours in
their exhibition of acquisitions in September 1982
and included a number of her works in the Irish
Women Artists Exhibition in 1987.

In August 1987 the Crawford Municipal Art
Gallery in Cork put on a Mildred Anne Butler
exhibition showing over one hundred of her

Oak at Pond Walk

Among the Woods

watercolours and drawings together with the last remaining three of her sketch books and some photographs from an old family album. Reviews in the national press, radio and television confirmed that this was indeed the rediscovery of a genius. The exhibition went on to the National Gallery of Ireland in December 1987 and stayed there for six weeks where again it was seen by many thousands of people. Exhibitions have since been held in Belfast and Limerick and in the Royal Hospital, Kilmainham.

Now, nearly one hundred years after these watercolours were painted, we have a perfect record of rural life through the eyes of this great Edwardian lady. A woman walking in a village street carrying a bucket of water; washer women scrubbing clothes on washboards by a stream; a cockerel greeting the early morning outside a humble cottage door. Scenes of market squares in European towns such as Freiburg and romantic fountains in Paris give an added dimension. All these watercolours survive as a social history of the life and time of the settled Irish landowner and of the priveleged lady who dedicated herself to what then had become an accepted profession for a lady of her class.

Vivacious and evocative, her watercolours and sketches lean towards a quiet nostalgia, and the tranquility and Edwardian flavour of her life at Kilmurry is captured perfectly. Although of an earlier period than Alice Taylor's country childhood, they complement the sense of harmony with nature which has evoked such a response to her book, *To School Through The Fields*. As this present age retreats a little from the hysteria of a chaotic world many will find solace in the quiet paintings of Mildred Anne Butler.

~ July

THIS MONTH IS the heart of the summer. If the heat is to come it is here now and holiday-makers swell the population. People leave the cities for the cool of the country and the seaside.

Oh! the pain of the city street
The crowd
The noise
And the burning heat.
Oh! the joy of a mossy stream
Cool grass
And trees
And no human being.

Now the countryside wears her finery with the confidence of a woman in the full bloom of her beauty. In the woods the trees merge into each other, so over-grown are they in the full flush of their growth. All the farm houses are empty as the residents are out in the fields. Cows come back for milking morning and evening but sleep out in the fields at night beneath the moon. The calves have abandoned their straw-filled houses and now roam the green fields, enjoying their freedom. Sometimes they come under attack from the gadfly, which causes them, with tails held high, to stampede down the hill to seek shelter under the overhanging sally trees in the cool of the river. They drive the brown trout to seek shelter in a deeper pool further down, away from their flipping tails and kicking legs.

In the meadows the hay is saved and the ditches are like brides adorned with honeysuckle hedges. The countryside is alive with a celebration of beauty. Now you can stay out late at night, sitting on the river bank, watching the fish jump, because the night is balmy and cold is a forgotten memory. The wild roses are in full bloom on the arching briars, asking to be picked but sinking their sharp, hidden thorns into your unwary fingers if you dare presume to do so. The countryside is full of sensuous beauty offering all her abundance to satisfy our appetites.

Little birds attempting to fly, flutter between branches, while the supervising mother watches from nearby. She does not intervene when baby sinks to the ground because in nature the young must learn to look after themselves and soon he is making his way, daily higher and higher. The goslings from the farmyard parade daily to the river where they swim in a. shallow pool with the fiercely protective gander and the gentle goose. The goslings are soft and floppy-footed, sometimes losing balance they topple over to be righted again by the vigilant father. The ducks, too, quack their way to the river but keep a safe distance from the gander. In the haggard the hens are busily scratching and with fluffed out feathers use their wings as additional scratchers; they rise clouds of dust in their energetic pursuit to provide tasty titbits for their chicks. The hen alone is faithful to the confines of the farmyard and will never wander far afield, except the odd maverick who will stray a little further to an outlying hedge to lay her eggs and hatch her chicks out unsupervised. She takes the chance of becoming the victim of the ever-wandering fox.

And so all nature plays out its drama on the open stage of July, when the full cast is in action, providing its own chorus line, background music and all the central characters.

♪ July

July

July

July

July

July

August

TO ME AUGUST will always be the month of the white butterflies. A few years ago a very close friend died suddenly and took part of my heart with him. The morning of his funeral I went into his garden, his own special place that he had loved so much in life. The sunrise sparkled on the dewy cobwebs, the veil of heaven was still spread over the earth. As I sat there surrounded by the earthly expression of his love the white butterflies flew around me. Closing my eyes, I knew that he was there, because this was the place while still on earth where he found his peace and communicated with God.

Later that day when we laid him to rest in the sun-warmed earth, the butterflies came again. They carried my thoughts from the grief of the physical parting to a higher level. There is but a veil of white butterflies between us and those we love.

This is the time of year when nature, having developed to the full, is maturing in the warmth of the August sun. Growth has turned into ripening and restfullness is abroad. The feverish activity of spring and summer has slowed in the lethargic heat of smouldering August. Now the honey is taken from the hives and extracted to run in liquid gold into the honey pots that will bring the taste of summer to the winter months. The aroma of jam making fills the farm kitchen and pots of rich, dark coloured jam line the store cupboard with the secret of summer wine. The housewife is reaping the harvest of the earth.

Our bodies, too, need the golden warmth of the sun and how lovely it is to see bronze-skinned children playing on the sea-shore exulting in the joyous freedom that the wide expanse of sea and sand affords.

Across the golden amber sand

I saw the sunlit sea
The waves were sparkling in the sun
And laughing back at me
Out they danced and in they raced
And tumbled in the caves
I think that I shall never see
Such happy things as waves.

Holidays begin when we turn the key in the door
and sit into the car, not when we arrive at our
destination. Over-excited children can sometimes
be a handful on a long car journey but children
have a great sense of anticipation.

The joy of
Anticipation
Awaiting dreams'
Realisation
Looking forward
Is the fun
Of happy things
Yet to come.

There is an expression in yoga: "Enjoy the
journey." Children do not need to study yoga to do
this.

August closes the curtains on the summer scene
and turns our eyes to the season of "mists and
mellow fruitfullness." We are at the crossroads
with two views and it looks good in both
directions, the warmth of the summer leads us into
the richness of autumn. The countryside that was
beautiful is about to become magnificent.

August

August

August

August

August

♪ August

September

THE YEAR HAS turned
Its coat of youth
Maturing into
Mellow hues
Its growing pains
And burning heat
Cooling now
To calmer days.

This is the month of the blackberries: the long, thorny briars that were enemies for the rest of the year now redeem themselves with luscious peace offerings. They arch themselves across the ditches and hedges and drape themselves to the ground, so laden are they with black juicy bounty. When you pick them they overflow on to your fingers, baptising them with their deep red wine. A bucket full of berries is a dark, rich promise. No other jam holds summer in its flavour like the blackberry; dark with the warmth of the sun, it is the queen of the store cupboard.

The apples, too, come into their own at this time of the year; golden or red, they peep out from between the green leaves of the apple tree. A tree laden with apples is a glorious sight to behold and when an overripe one hits the ground with a soft thud it is a signal to the birds and bees that juicy fruit is waiting for them. In our orchard, when I was young, the pigs loved a feed of windfalls. The slightest wind brought the heavy overripe apples cascading down and the pigs gathered, drawn almost by a sixth sense, and gobbled them up, grunting and snorting with appreciation. Pigs have a good sense of enjoyment and if you have ever watched a pig roll around in soft, oozing mud and seen the look of bliss on his face, it is a picture of total mental and physical relaxation. The pig is an animal who is often dismissed as a lesser species but if you ever try to drive one of them somewhere that he does not want to go you will see exercises of brain power to outwit Einstein and positive thinking to out-think Norman Vincent Peale.

At this time of year, 29 September to be exact, country people celebrated Michaelmas with the killing of the first goose of the year. Then the geese were judged to be at their peak, young and fleshy, and providing the family with a succulent meal in honour of St Michael.

Now the squirrel gathers his nuts in preparation for the winter. The farmer, like the squirrel, must also provide for the winter, otherwise his animals cannot cope with the bare days ahead when the fields no longer provide the needful.

Schools now all over the country open up their doors to welcome back reluctant children. After running free for the summer months they must now be housed up. Mothers with tears in their eyes watch the tiny tots take their first steps into the adult world.

> How it hurts to see him go
> My babe of tender years
> Clutching at his little sack
> Choking back his tears
> I long to shelter in my arms
> My little lad turned four
> But I must take his hand
> And lead him out the door
> I must learn to let him go
> Just helping when I can
> My little son now taking
> His first steps to being a man.

So September, while bringing to a close the warm days, is the beginning of the academic year, and for the little children beginning school it is the opening up of a whole new world.

September

September

September

September

September

♪ September

♪ October

THIS IS THE most relaxed month of the year. Like the autumn of life, the struggle is over and the peace of maturity spreads the essence of golden October over the land. No matter where you live, you should make time to walk through woods at this time of year. Here in Innishannon we are surrounded by woods on both sides of the river and to drive along the road by the river from Bandon to Innishannon and on to Kinsale must surely be one of the most glorious drives in the country. Though driving is not the ideal way to enjoy the woods, sometimes it is the only opportunity people have so "when all fruit fails, welcome haws." But one of the advantages of driving through the scenic valley is that you get to see the long expanse of woodside, and when you think that there can be nothing more beautiful than the view at Dundaniel Castle you come to the view at Innishannon Bridge and then down along Shippool Castle on to Kinsale. The trees are multi-coloured in a glorious profusion of golden browns, reds and yellows. They form a soft, voluptuous, panoramic view and give you the illusion that you could sink into their softness. Mother nature is providing us with a visual feast and, like all mothers, is making us feel that life is good.

Walking through the wood now is like walking through the land of whispers. All around you hear the rustle of the falling leaves, breathing their last as they glide earthwards. A soft breeze sends the branches creaking and more leaves drift down. There is the rustling of birds in the ivy-clad stone walls; in the undergrowth rabbits and other four-legged residents scurry about. This is the whispering world of the wood and we should always remember we are only visitors: like all good guests, we should not disturb the occupants and should leave no evidence of our visit.

Some people find this time of year sad - summer over, winter coming - but I think that it is one of the most beautiful times of the year. The mist of an early October morning is like the soft dew of Heaven resting on the earth. As the mists begin to lift, the trees seem to rise out of the earth like Our Lord ascending into Heaven. Horses grazing in the field, shrouded in the early morning mist that sometimes blankets them and then rises, gives them an almost mystical quality. It puts one in mind of Fionn, Oisín and the Fianna and maybe dreams of Tir Na nOg. It is a scene of swirling mists with ethereal forms appearing and disappearing.

Woods at this time of year are beautiful but a great tree standing in splendid isolation in the centre of a large field has a majesty all its own. A few years ago, going to the All-Ireland Final, we drove through Kilkenny to call on the Design Centre. I went in the gate of Kilkenny Castle afterwards and there, away to the left, stood a huge tree.

You stood there
In splendid isolation
A remote stillness
Centered in a green field
Your praying arms
Held forth
In majestic supplication
Shrouded in your
Green leafy veils
Of mysterious depths
What a tranquil untouchable
World of nature
You portray.

October

October

October

October

October

October

♫ November

MY MOTHER NEVER mentioned November without adding - the month of the Holy Souls. They were part of her November, all her relations gone on out of her world but not forgotten. She prayed for them and had Masses said for them every November. She had, and still has, her own list of religious institutions that she contributes to regularly. My father called them her "holy men." He never sent them anything and often teased her about them. He always said that a Mass you attended yourself was far more valuable than any contributions, to which my mother would reply serenely, "Nothing to stop us having it both ways." My father loved arguing - or debating as he perferred to call it - but he got no satisfaction out of trying to get the better of my mother. She belonged to the "I'm on my way to Heaven and I shall not be moved" brigade. They are the people who, having listened to all sides of the argument, follow their own gut instincts. She would break the heart of any liberated theologian because, having listened to him and told him he was propably quite right, she would do exactly as she saw fit herself.

Maybe the fact that November is the month for remembering the dead has a natural source, because now the earth is starting to curl up and go to sleep for the winter. The first frost usually comes and the last of the flowers burn up and die. But the November air has a sharp, invigorating tang and often the trees that are not yet quite bare have a rigid beauty on a frosty November morning, the remaining leaves fluttering like silent birds on the bare branches.

Usually the first fires are lit and they bring a sense of togetherness into the family home; even if you are on your own, a house with a crackling fire is not quite so empty. Gazing into the fire of logs and turf, one can see flickering, imaginary pictures. You can untangle many a problem in the warm glow of a good fire. My idea of luxury is sitting on a rug before a warm fire, with a tea tray and a good book and no distractions. My other idea of luxury is breakfast in bed with the morning paper and nothing waiting to be done. Neither of these appeal in the summer but with the winter drawing in they are comforting thoughts.

For children, Halloween has its own special magic of barm brack and spooks and dressing up. We did not have the luxury of barm brack when I was young but we had the bonus of going out and picking our own nuts and apples. I suppose every era has its own pluses and minuses.

On the farm the cows were no longer let out after evening milking; the frosty grass was too chilly, so they swapped it for the comfortable staw-bedded stalls. Now, too, the heifers who had roamed free in the inches by the river were brought back to the farmyard for the first time since they had left it as calves in May. They were very nervous and difficult to get into the stalls and tied up. My father lost patience with them fast and his "farmyard language" came into play. He used descriptive phrases new to the English language and when the animals were finally housed he raised he eyes to Heaven and declared: "If ever a man suffered." As far as my father was concerned, he had the prerogative on suffering in our hourse.

So in November all the farm activities returned to the farmyard where the animals were gathered in from the cold. The horses were the last to leave the field but even they, too, came back to the stables by night.

November

November

November

November

♪ November

November

ᔦ December

CHRISTMAS IS THE warm glow in the heart of the winter and the month of December is focused on it. I am sad when I hear people say in desperation, in mid-December, that there are so many shopping days to Christmas. They are building Christmas into a commercial crescendo and often when it peaks the bubble bursts and Christmas has no heart. Commercialism and Christmas are inseparable but we should try to maintain the balance. Christmas is the birthday of Jesus and in buying presents we are celebrating with His friends and ours, but without Him it is a meaningless exercise.

My mother had a great sense of Christmas and it had nothing to do with money because money was scarce in those days. The plucking of the geese, though we did not enjoy doing it, still held a sense of anticipation. It was the first step. Then there was the going to the wood for the holly and peeling the ivy off the bark of the old trees and looking forward to decorating the house, which we were free to do exactly as we pleased. It did not bother her how it looked as long as we enjoyed it. My father was dispatched to pick out the largest turnip from the turnip pit and we scrubbed it clean and then he bored a hole to take the tall white candle. My mother always insisted on red berry holly for the candle, it was a must as far as she was concerned and we often trudged across frosty fields to a distant wood so that her candle could rise tall and elegant from a growth of red berry holly. We had a sense of pride when the candle was lit because we had helped to gather the holly that now glistened in the candlelight. She had what she termed "Christmas mottoes": they were unframed Christmas scenes and each year they appeared in their usual corner. One, I remember, depicted Santa filling the children's stockings by an old fashioned fire just like ours. It was very easy to imagine that my stocking was amongst them. Another had a raised paper crib with yellow straw trailing over the sides of the manger where a plump, happy baby Jesus smiled between a cow and a donkey.

Lighting the Christmas candle officially opened the festivities. It sat on the uncurtained window around which we all gathered in a semi-circle, my father holding a box of matches, my mother with a bottle of Holy Water. When the candle was lighting she sprinkled us with Holy Water and we all blessed ourselves. Because she was a bit generous with the Holy Water, my father, who had a bald head, finished up his sign of the cross by wiping his head with his cap and demanding, "Are you trying to bless us or baptise us?"

Each Christmas had the same ritual which gave to it a sense of occasion. So much part of my Christmas did all this tradition become that I now do just as my mother did in my home. In such ways are old customs continued.

The spirit of Christmas is to be found in many places and it means different things to different people. To me, it is in the countryside at dusk on Christmas Eve when I go out for a walk and absorb the peace around me because I think that the spirit of Christmas rests in the quiet places of the mind. So this Christmas Eve go out by yourself in the stillness of the night and out there under the stars is the real meaning of Christmas.

December

♪ December

♪ December

December

♪ December

December

Notes

♪ Notes

Notes

♪ Notes

Notes

♪ Notes

Addresses

Addresses

Addresses

Addresses

Addresses

Addresses

Addresses

Addresses

Addresses

Addresses

Addresses

Addresses

Addresses

Addresses

Addresses

Addresses